Appointment with Action

Contents

Speed and

Written by Kerrie Capobianco

Action

Many different people are race car drivers.
Some drivers are men, and some drivers are women.
Some drivers are old, and some drivers are young.
But all these people like to drive fast around the track.

There are lots of different racetracks.
Some are paved tracks, and some are dirt tracks.
Some are straight tracks, and some are curved tracks.
Some are long tracks, and some are short tracks.

Race cars are different, too.
They are made for the tracks
they will be driven on
and the speeds they will be driven at.
But they all have to be very safe.

All race car drivers go to a car racing school.
They are shown how to turn and pass and stop.
They are shown how to drive safely at fast speeds.
They are shown what to do if they crash.
They have to learn all these things
because driving a race car is risky.

All race car drivers must wear a seat belt.
The seat belt in a race car
is different than the one in your car.
A race car seat belt has five straps.
Two straps come over the shoulders.
Two go around the middle.
One comes between the legs.
All the straps go into one buckle.
This makes it easy for the driver
to get out of the car if there is a crash.

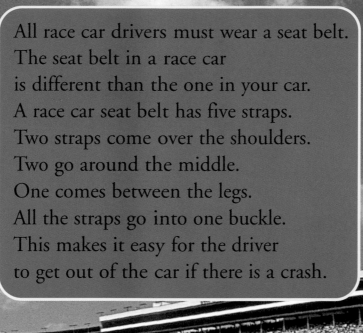

There are a lot of race car crashes.
The crashes may happen
because the driver is going too fast.
The crashes may happen
because part of the car breaks down or blows up.
Sometimes the car will go off the track,
crash into a wall, and even flip over!

A lot of race cars catch on fire when they crash.

Which are
the big race car
events
in the world?

Race car drivers wear special suits, special gloves, and special shoes. These special clothes keep them safe if a car catches on fire.
Race car drivers wear helmets, too. The helmet keeps the driver's head safe if the car crashes.

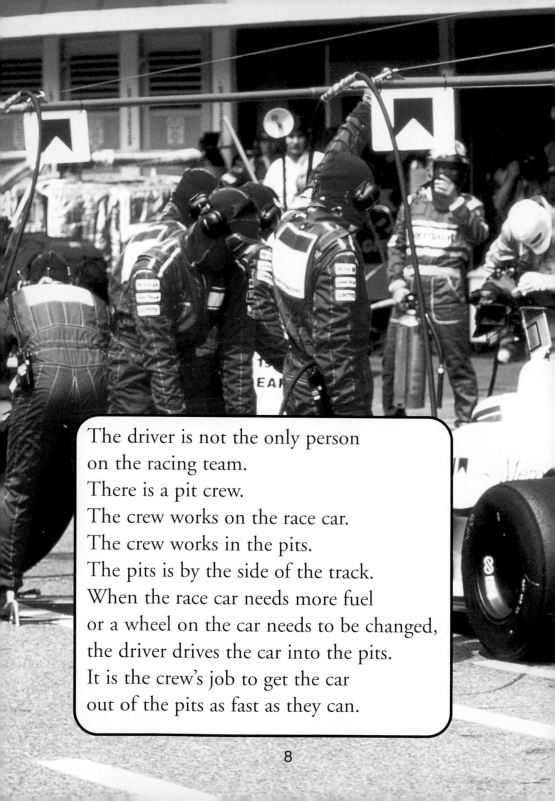

The driver is not the only person
on the racing team.
There is a pit crew.
The crew works on the race car.
The crew works in the pits.
The pits is by the side of the track.
When the race car needs more fuel
or a wheel on the car needs to be changed,
the driver drives the car into the pits.
It is the crew's job to get the car
out of the pits as fast as they can.

What training would you need to be a race car driver?

If you are a person
who wants a life of taking risks and driving fast,
maybe you could be a race car driver.

Whirlybirds

Written by David Lowe
Illustrated by Mark Wilson

The waves crashed up onto the rocks
as the tide was coming in.
My mother and I were starting to get wet.
My mother started to yell and wave her arms.
She had seen my father on the beach.
He could see that we were stuck on the rocks.
He ran to our car to use his phone.
Then he ran back to the beach.

The sea was getting closer to us.
We were both cold and wet.
I did not cry.
I knew my father had called for help.

Then I heard a funny noise
coming from above.
I looked up.
There was a rescue helicopter
– a whirlybird.
A voice asked if we were hurt.
We waved to let them know we were OK.
A woman came down to us
on a long rope from the helicopter.
The woman had a harness
and life jacket around her,
and another harness
and life jacket in her hands.
The woman put the harness
and life jacket on me.
Then I was going up, up on the rope
and into the helicopter.
I was very scared.

In the helicopter, a man gave me a blanket
to help me get warm.
Soon my mother was next to me.
The woman who had saved us was there, too.
We said thank you to the woman.
My mother had some cuts on her legs from the rocks.
The man put some bandages on her legs
and gave her a blanket.

We landed safely back on the beach.
My father ran over to the helicopter.
My father said thank you to the people
from the rescue helicopter.
I had always wanted to take a ride in a whirlybird,
but not like that.
Being stuck on the rocks was no fun at all.

Why
do you think
helicopters
can be called
whirlybirds?

13

Rescue Helicopters

All around the world, lots of lives
are saved by rescue helicopters.
They can get help
to sick and hurt people on boats at sea.
They can pick up shipwrecked people.
They can lift people and animals away from floods.
They can pick up people stuck or hurt
in the mountains.

They take people badly hurt
from road crashes to the hospital.
Sometimes they can help find lost people.

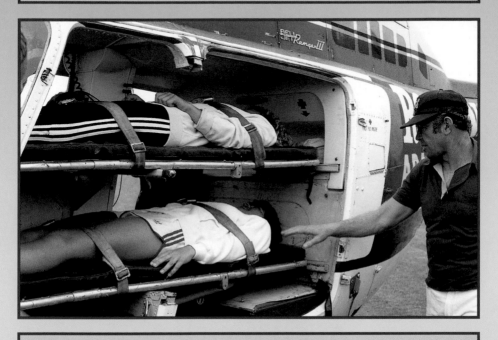

Whirlybirds are good for all this work.
They do not need a lot of space
to take off and land.
They can fly in tricky places.
They can fly close to the ground.
They can fly fast and slow.
They can fly backwards and forwards.
Best of all, helicopters can stay still in the air.

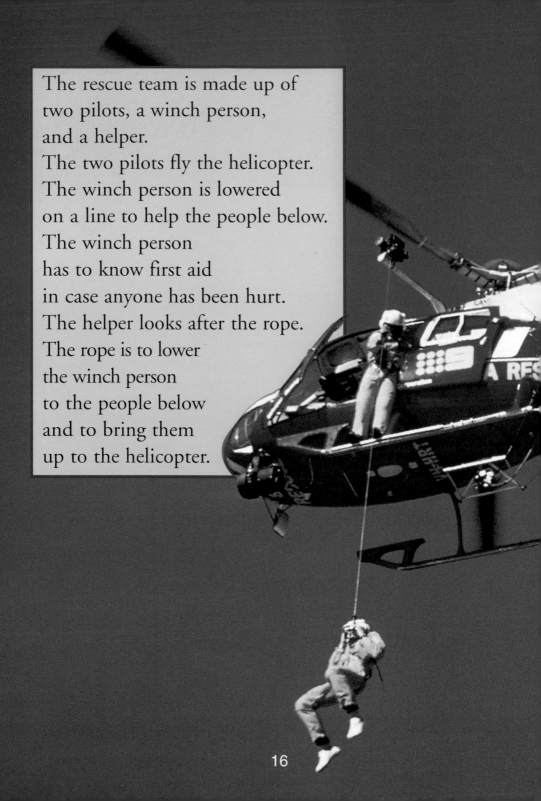

The rescue team is made up of
two pilots, a winch person,
and a helper.
The two pilots fly the helicopter.
The winch person is lowered
on a line to help the people below.
The winch person
has to know first aid
in case anyone has been hurt.
The helper looks after the rope.
The rope is to lower
the winch person
to the people below
and to bring them
up to the helicopter.

At sea, the winch person needs
life jackets and waterproof clothes.
In the mountains,
the winch person needs
warm clothes and climbing boots.
Food, water, and sleeping bags
are always on the rescue helicopter
in case the winch person has to stay
with the hurt person.

**What training
would you need
to become
a rescue pilot?**

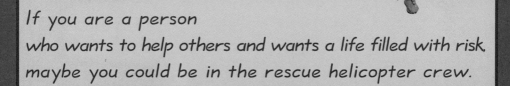

If you are a person
who wants to help others and wants a life filled with risk,
maybe you could be in the rescue helicopter crew.

What do you think a smoke jumper does?

Smoke Jumpers

Written by Kerrie Capobianco

Each year, there are many forest fires all over the world.

Today, we have many ways of fighting forest fires,
but many years ago it was very different.

Before 1940, if there was a forest fire,
firefighters had only two ways of getting to the fire.
They could drive their trucks, or they could walk.
Sometimes big areas of trees burned down
before firefighters got there.
Sometimes houses burned down
before firefighters got there.

Today, firefighters can get to forest fires by plane.
Some firefighters are trained to jump out of planes
with parachutes on.
This is a much faster way to get to the forest fires.
These firefighters are called smoke jumpers.

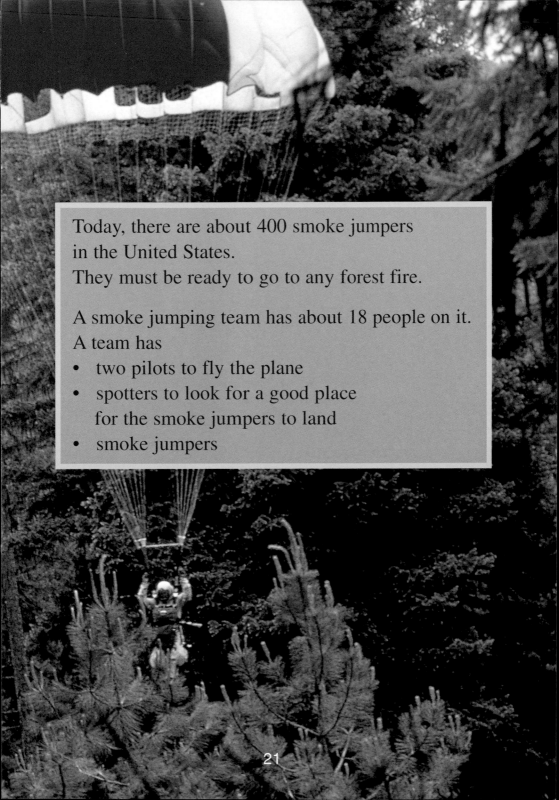

Today, there are about 400 smoke jumpers
in the United States.
They must be ready to go to any forest fire.

A smoke jumping team has about 18 people on it.
A team has
- two pilots to fly the plane
- spotters to look for a good place
  for the smoke jumpers to land
- smoke jumpers

Two smoke jumpers work together to put the fire out.
When the smoke jumpers land in the forest,
the spotters throw down food, water, and tools.

Smoke jumpers do not put out the forest fires.
They stop the fires from getting bigger.
They dig a fireline.
A fireline is like a drain around the fire.
The smoke jumpers clear away all of the trees
and plants near the fireline until there is just bare earth.
Then the fire will burn out because it has nothing to burn.

Being a smoke jumper is hard.
All smoke jumpers have to be in good health.
They have to work close to the fire
where it is very hot.
If the fire is very big,
the smoke jumpers have to work long hours.
They do not get to rest.
Even when they are tired and want to go home,
they must stay in the forest.
They have to stay until they have done their job.

If you are a person
who wants a life filled with challenge and danger,
maybe you could be a smoke jumper.

Dillon's Dream

Written by Suzanne Chambers
Illustrated by David Pearson

Dillon was stock car crazy.
Dillon's dad had a purple stock car
called "The Brooster".
Dillon loved The Brooster
because it went really fast.
Dillon's dad and The Brooster
had made it to the finals of the stock car races.

The week before the finals,
Dillon and his dad worked hard on The Brooster.
They checked the engine.
They checked the wheels and the oil.
They wanted everything to be right.

The night before the race,
Dillon dreamed his dad had won.
The prize was a stock car like The Brooster
but the right size for Dillon.
Dillon was about to race away in it
when his mother woke him.

At the Darlington raceway, Dillon and his dad
checked The Brooster one last time.
They wanted to win the race.
They wanted The Brooster
to be the fastest stock car in the race.
Dad put on his racing clothes,
and Dillon checked Dad's helmet.
Dad was ready for the race.
Dillon and his mother went off
to watch The Brooster race.

All the cars lined up at the starting line.
Then they were off with a loud bang.
The Brooster was out in front.
Dust was flying everywhere as the cars raced past.
All the people were clapping and cheering.
As the cars went around the curve,
The Brooster was still in the lead.
But some of the other cars were very close.
A green car called "Irish Moss"
came up on the inside and overtook The Brooster.

"Go, Dad!" Dillon yelled. "Faster! Faster!"

Dillon was jumping and yelling for his dad.
A red stock car raced past the other cars
and was behind The Brooster.

What are stock cars?

26

Bang!
Smoke was everywhere.
The green car had spun off the track
and flipped over onto its top.

"Ohhhh," yelled the crowd.

Dillon's dad roared past and waved to Dillon.
Dillon knew that this meant the driver was all right.

The Brooster was in the lead again,
but the red stock car was catching up.
A blue stock car came up fast.
The blue stock car overtook the red stock car.
It was behind The Brooster.

What would you need to learn to become a stock car driver?

All the cars roared around the last curve.

"Go, Dad!" Dillon yelled. "Go! Go! Go!"

Then the Brooster made a funny noise
and slowed down.
The red stock car roared past
The Brooster and blue stock car.
The red stock car went across the finish line.
The red car had won the race!

Dillon was so sad.
His dad had almost won.
But when Dillon found his dad, he was smiling.

"Why are you so happy?" asked Dillon.

"You'll see," said his dad,
as they walked to the winner's circle.

The driver of the red stock car got a big silver cup.

"Bruce Goodheart driving The Brooster gets
the second prize," said the judge.
"But Bruce has asked if his son Dillon could come up
and get the prize."

As Dillon walked up to the stage,
a woman took his hand and led him to the other side.

There in front of him was a little yellow stock car,
just like the one in his dream.

"What will you call it?"
asked his mother.

"Dillon's Dream," said Dillon.

What other names could Dillon have called the car?

*If you are a person
who wants a life filled with fast cars and excitement,
maybe you could be a stock car driver.*

Glossary

🐾 **firebreak** – a place where plants are dug out so that a fire has no fuel to burn

🐾 **first aid** – the help given to a person who is sick, or hurt, before they reach a doctor or hospital

🐾 **pit crew** – the people who look after the racing cars when they pull into the pits area beside the racetrack

🐾 **pits** – the place by the side of a racetrack where racing cars go to be fixed, or get fuel

🐾 **smoke jumpers** – firefighters who parachute from aircraft to fight fires

🐾 **spotters** – firefighters who spot, from the air, the places for smoke jumpers to land and fight fires

🐾 **stock car** – a race car made for car racing where collisions and crashes are part of the race

🐾 **whirlybird** – another name for a helicopter